Do you admire the men and women who
have gone into the wilderness
and carved out empires with their bare hands?

Do you idolize people who
have pulled themselves up by their own bootstraps
and gone on to win fame and fortune?

Do you revere those who
have had the courage of their convictions,
and triumphed over insurmountable odds?

Do you long to attain wealth and success
through hard work, perseverance,
and the strength of your own ambition?

Well, you'll never accomplish
anything like that
if you waste valuable time
reading trash like . . .

THE SELF-MADE

MAD

. . . But you may have yourself a few laughs!

More **MAD** Humor from **SIGNET**

William M. Gaines's

THE SELF-MADE

MAD

Albert B. Feldstein, editor

A SIGNET BOOK from

NEW AMERICAN LIBRARY

TIMES MIRROR

New York and Toronto

The New English Library Limited, London

SIGNET TRADEMARK REG. U.S. PAT. OFF. AND FOREIGN COUNTRIES
REGISTERED TRADEMARK—MARCA REGISTRADA
HECHO EN CHICAGO, U.S.A.

SIGNET, SIGNET CLASSICS, MENTOR AND PLUME BOOKS
are published *in the United States* by
The New American Library, Inc.,
1301 Avenue of the Americas, New York, New York 10019,
in Canada by The New American Library of Canada Limited,
295 King Street East, Toronto 2, Ontario,
in the United Kingdom by The New English Library Limited,
Barnard's Inn, Holborn, London, E.C. 1, England

PRINTED IN THE UNITED STATES OF AMERICA

CONTENTS

Fishing is one of the most popular outdoor sports in the world today. Oddly enough, it is indulged in mostly by men. Let us examine Fishing, and attempt to discover what is the magic power that draws millions of men into this sport every year. Can it be that they seek a source of food? No, because they'd starve to death on the average catch! Can it be that they seek

FISH

GOOD FISHING EQUIPMENT IS A PREREQUISITE FOR CATCHING BIG FISH

POORLY EQUIPPED FISHERMAN

to improve their health? No, because they usually come home exhausted, insect-bitten and sun-burned! Can it be that they seek the opportunity to sit and meditate on the philosophies of life? No, because they often get so swacked on beer, they can't even meditate on which end of the rod to hold! Can it be that they seek to get away from their wives and kids? You said it! That's the real reason men go . . .

ING

To be a good fisherman, the first thing one needs (aside from a desire to get away from certain irritants like job and family) is to be well-equipped.

**WELL
EQUIPPED
FISHERMAN**

CONVINCING PROOF
THAT GOOD
FISHING EQUIPMENT
CATCHES BIG FISH

**THERE ARE
MANY WONDERFUL
KINDS OF FISHING.**

LET US EXPLORE EACH...

FRESH WATER

Fresh water fishing is best in remote
areas. That's why a true fresh water

From the outset, nature presents a formidable barrier to
the intrepid fresh water fisherman . . . but he pushes on.

But it's all worth-while, because when at last he arrives
at his secret, hidden, remote "fisherman's paradise", he

FISHING

fisherman is willing to suffer **extreme** hardships for a taste of this sport.

Through impenetrable wilderness, infested with dangers at every turn, the true fresh water fisherman fights his way.

feels a deep emotional sense of closeness to nature . . . and an even deeper sense of closeness to other fishermen.

CASTING

The grace and balance and timing required in casting is equal to that of a ballet dancer. In short, it's an art!

Unfortunately, there are about as many artful fresh water fishermen around these days as there are ballet dancers.

WATER FISHING

EXPERIMENTING

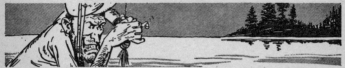

Trying out a secret new bait or lure is always a thrill —

Especially when the fisherman discovers one that works —

EXPLORING

Finding a new, uncharted fishing spot is often rewarding.

HAZARDS OF FRESH

CARELESS USE OF EQUIPMENT

Fishing requires a high degree of concentration, thus an orderly arrangement of equipment is necessary. This fisherman carelessly hung bait box where lunch box should be.

LANDING A FISH

Sometimes, the fresh water fisherman has quite a struggle on his hands before he can get a fish into his creel. It is often amazing how much fight these little guys put up.

WATER FISHING

NETTING A FISH

Panic is greatest problem in netting fish. Often fishermen panic, and . . .

forget to bring fish in close before netting it. Instead, they'll chase it

. . . sometimes with disastrous results.

DEEP SEA

On a deep sea fishing boat, one is likely to encounter some of the world's weirdest creatures. And one is likely to encounter some pretty strange ones in the ocean, too; The goal of every deep sea sport fisherman is to land a really big fish. Sometimes he will battle for hours to

A THRILLING MOMENT

Deep sea fishing is exciting

HOW DEEP SEA

Big deep sea fish must be played till they are completely exhausted before they can be gaffed and hoisted aboard.

FISHING

achieve that goal. Yes, nothing can match the excitement of a 160 pound man pitted against a struggling, thrashing monster who wants to prevent him from reaching his goal. But when his wife finally gives in and lets him go, the battle is well worth it . . .

IN DEEP SEA FISHING

because the catch has no size limit.

FISHING WORKS

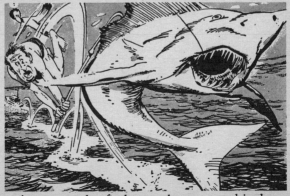

Here is an example of what can happen to a big deep sea fish when it is gaffed before it is completely exhausted.

PARTY BOAT

There are various other names for this type of fishing. These public boats are either chartered by private groups, who come aboard with a big supply of food and a bigger supply of liquor, or they are

PARTY BOAT MELVIN
Going Out For MACKEREL!
COMING BACK WITH EMPTY BEER CANS, WHISKEY BOTTLES, AND ONE OR TWO LESS PASSENGERS

As soon as party boat passengers

HOW PARTY BOAT

Party boat fishermen crowd each side of the boat and drop their lines . . .

As soon as they feel a tug on their line, they reel in frantically . . .

FISHING

filled with individuals at so much per head, who come aboard with a big supply of food and a bigger supply of liquor. In both cases, the term "party boat" fits.

are loaded, things get under way.

FISHING WORKS

. . . only to find they've hooked the lines of the guys from the other side.

SMALL BOAT

THE "PRIVATE"

THE "RENTED"

FISHING

SMALL BOAT

SMALL BOAT

MISCELLANEOUS

CLEANING THE FISH

To fully enjoy fishing, the enthusiast must be adept at cleaning the fish he brings home, if he knows what's good for him! Start with a sharp knife. First, scale the fish.

Then remove the tail, the fins, and finally the head. Now reach in and pull out the air sack, the liver, the heart, the intestines, the . . . ulp . . . intestines . . . ghack . . .

FACTS ABOUT FISHING

FILLETING THE FISH

Many fishermen prefer to fillet their fish, that is: to remove all of the bones and other inedible parts, leaving only the sweet succulent meat. Filleting a fish is an art. Here we see a fish before and after it has been filleted.

BEFORE FILLETING

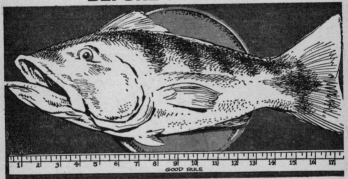

AFTER FILLETING

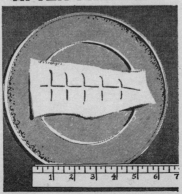

MOUNTING THE FISH AS TROPHIES

RIGHT WAY TO MOUNT A FISH

WRONG WAY TO MOUNT A FISH

Mounted fish make for an interesting display. Fishermen should try to mount one of every variety they've caught.

TYPES OF BAIT

There are almost as many types of bait as there are fish in the sea. Here are some popular types . . .

Lure

Tied Fly

Untied Fly

Live Bait

Dead Bait

Sure-Fire Bait

Jail Bait

Jail Bait Lure

OFF SEASON EXERCISES
To keep in proper shape, there is one set of exercises

ARM EXERCISES

Grasp heavy weights firmly, and lift up and down for one hour every day.

Grasp heavy weights and swing outward to the sides for one hour every day.

HOW ARM EXERCISES HELP

They help when telling off-season fish stories,

FOR FISHERMEN
the fisherman must indulge in . . . mainly . . .

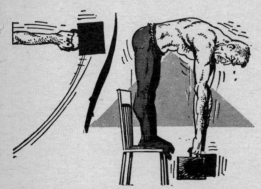

Grasp heavy weights and hang over the edge of a chair for 1 hour every day.

FISHERMEN DURING OFF SEASON

because the arms are stretched to revolting length!

END

In a world generally prone to discard the outmoded, we can't figure out how the Olympic Games have survived virtually unchanged since ancient times. After all, how much of a demand is there for discus hurlers, shot putters, and javelin

MAD'S OLYMPIC

1500 METER
TAXICAB DASH

An event restricted to city dwellers of all competing nations only, as it can be dangerous for the untrained. Contestants dash 1500 meters while being chased by entire fleet of Yellow Cabs. Any entry who's killed is immediately disqualified.

throwers these days? Why not modernize the Olympic events so that the long hours of training won't be wasted in later life? For greater excitement, plus practicality, here is a run-down of events we propose for . . .

MODERN GAMES

DO-IT-YOURSELF
DECATHALON

Amateur Handymen throughout the world compete in ten different "do-it-yourself" projects. Object is to hold down medical payments for injuries to not more than five times the cost of having same ten projects done by competent professionals.

8:14 COMMUTER
HOP, STEP AND JUMP

Open to amateur commuters of the world. Contestants arrive at suburban station at 8:14. Object is to catch commuter train which left at 8:13. 2 points for catching train, and 1 point for getting close enough to throw briefcase aboard.

TV SANDWICH
MARATHON

Open to qualified television viewers of all nations. Competitors vie in race to see which one can make most complicated sandwich, dashing from living room TV set to kitchen and back to living room, all in space of a one-minute commercial.

NEWSPAPER HURLING

Open to paper boys of all nations. Each contestant hurls ten papers at a porch from a distance of 20 yards. Winner is decided on basis of 2 points for landing paper in puddle, 1 point for sailing it in shrubbery, minus-1 for hitting porch.

DEPOSIT BOTTLE
MARATHON

Open to husbands of all nations who live at least 3 blocks from a grocery store. Object is to carry as many empty bottles as possible without breaking any. Those contestants who abandon them in an alley, pretending that they aren't theirs, lose.

100 METER PICNIC LUNCH DASH

Object is to prevent picnic lunch from being ruined when cloudburst begins. All contestants must run 100 meters to car, carrying baskets, only to discover keys are locked inside. The winner is chosen for both ingenuity and colorful language.

BUFFERIN
ASSIMILATING

Open to athletes of all countries with perfected stomach trap doors (amateurs only). Object is to assimilate Bufferin into bloodstream faster than Aspirin or Anacin. Contest void if anybody loses a headache and develops an upset stomach.

HORN HONKING

Competitors vie to see who is quickest to blow horn at car ahead once stoplight turns green. World record (.003 sec.) set by late Waldo Furd of U.S.A. Mr. Furd succumbed to head blows administered by cab driver shortly after setting record.

WRONG NUMBER DIALING

Open to phoners to see who can dial most wrong numbers. Event run off at 4 A.M. 3 points awarded for reaching home with colicky baby, 2 for reaching home with dog who barks at ringing phones, and 1 for awakening doctor who just got to bed.

END

Any current or former Enlisted Man in the service knows all about Officers. They've learned the hard way! But we'll bet they don't know that, just as the Army publishes a basic "Soldiers Guide" for Enlisted Men, it also publishes a basic "Officer's Guide" for Commissioned Men. We know, because we got hold of a copy of this "Top Secret" document recently. Here, then, for the benefit of all the clods who may be going into service soon (so they'll know what to expect from their Officers) are excerpts from our version of

FM 21-46-239

THE U.S. ARMY CHICKEN OFFICER'S FIELD MANUAL

DEPARTMENT OF THE ARMY   TOP SECRET DOCUMENT

APRIL 1960

CONTENTS

CHAPTER 7
THE OFFICER'S CODE

Section 1: THE OFFICER'S GENERAL ORDERS

After your troops have taken an enemy town, cleaned out all pockets of resistance, set up guard posts along the perimeter, and the shooting has stopped, you, as an Officer, have an important job to do. Namely, climb out of that 27-foot-deep fox hole you've been hiding in.

You also have another important job: Obeying your Officer's General Orders. Here they are. Memorize them, and make sure they do not fall into enemy hands. Have an enlisted man swallow them.

1. To take charge of this enemy town, and all pretty girls in view, leaving the dogs for the men I outrank.
2. To ride my jeep through this town in a military manner, keeping always on the alert for crap games, available booze, and friendly planes that can take me out of danger in case of an enemy counter-attack.
3. To report all violations of black market orders I am instructed to enforce, so I can have more customers for my own supply of soap and Hershey bars.
4. To quit this town only when I am properly relieved, or if I get like frightened by an artillery shell landing 30 miles away.
5. To pass on to any Officer who relieves me: my feather bed, my hot water bottle, my pool table, my comic books, and my nine orderlies. But to be an Indian-Giver if I find out that I outrank him.
6. To talk to no one except in the line of duty, and to be so chicken that no one will talk to me even in the line of duty.
7. To give the alarm for help in case of attack, general disorder, or if I have like a bad war dream.
8. To call all Corporals to my room in any cases not covered by instructions, especially if they are WACS.
9. To insist that my men salute me at all times, and that they sleep and eat at attention, excusing only prostrate, wounded men whom I will have do push-ups while waiting to be evacuated to base hospitals.
10. To run to the General at every opportunity to repeat all the things my men call me, especially names like "Chicken" and "Fink", and try not to cry while doing so.

(Have your Orderly or 1st. Sergeant turn the page for you)

CHAPTER 8
MILITARY COURTESY

Section 1. TECHNIQUES OF THE HAND SALUTE

Depending upon your rank, and also upon the physical position you
will find yourself in during most of the day, your salutes may vary.
Here are the salute techniques for different ranking officers:

LIEUTENANTS

When saluting, you must stand tall,
raise your hand smartly until the tip
of your finger touches your headgear
slightly above your right eye. Then
drop your hand smartly to your side.

CAPTAINS AND MAJORS

You must sit up tall in your chair,
turn down the volume on your TV set,
raise hand smartly until tip of finger touches slightly above right eye.
Then drop hand smartly to your desk.

COLONELS

Lean back tall in your easy chair, push
WAC off lap, remove mood music
record from hi-fi set, put down glass
of bourbon, raise hand smartly until
tip of finger touches slightly below
right eye. Drop hand smartly to glass.

GENERALS

Lie back tall in your bed, cursing at
being disturbed so early in the after-
noon, raise your hand smartly until
the tip of your finger touches your
inter-office buzzer. Your orderly will
come in and salute smartly for you.

Section 11. WHEN TO LOOK FOR SALUTES

Any run-of-the-mill Officer can draw a salute from any run-of-the-mill enlisted man on a post. It is the "Creative Salute" that pays off for the really sincere "chicken" Officer.

Here are four of your best targets for "Creative Salutes":

(1) *An Enlisted Man, Living On Post, Carrying a Huge Bundle of Groceries.* Sneak up on him, step out quickly in front of him, show bars . . . then step nimbly aside allowing for smashing of eggs and other breakables on sidewalk as he raises his hand to salute you.

(2) *An Enlisted Man, Living On Post, Carrying Babies In Both Of His Arms.* Sneak up on him, step out quickly in front of him, and show bars as in (1). However, you will find that results are a lot more messier, a lot more noisier, and a heck of a lot more fun.

(3) *An Enlisted Man On Crutches Who Is Just Entering The Post Hospital.* Just make sure that you surprise your intended victim when he is going up steps or is in some awkward position. Otherwise, his crutches may not fall to the ground, and salute is wasted.

(4) *A Wounded Enlisted Man With Both Arms In Slings.* Since all he can do is squirm helplessly when you leap in front of him, he is an ideal target. Just remember: be gallant as well as stern. So open the door for him as he enters the Court Martial Trial Room.

CHAPTER 9
KEEPING PHYSICALLY FIT

Section 1. MARCHING

As an officer, you will be required to take long, arduous marches with your men. Here are some sound rules to follow to keep yourself physically fit during these long, arduous marches:

YOUR FEET

Make sure your feet are clean, and you are wearing clean socks. To keep up the circulation in your feet during the march, stamp them from time to time on the floor of your Jeep.

DRINKING

Ration your drinking carefully while on a march, as one canteen-full must usually last all the way. It is very difficult to refill canteens. There are few liquor stores on march routes.

FATIGUE

If you feel excessive fatigue, do not discontinue march. Instead, lean your head on your Jeep-driver's shoulder and go to sleep. He'll awaken you for your regular hourly ten minute break.

HALTS

During hourly 10-minute break, lean your head on your Jeep-driver's other shoulder, and go back to sleep. When break is over, he will awaken you in time for your hourly 40-minute nap.

SPECIAL WARNING: Be especially careful toward the end of a prolonged march when you get out of your Jeep to walk the 15 yards to your quarters. If you find yourself feeling dizzy and perspiring excessively during this hike, take a salt tablet.

CHAPTER 10
DECORATIONS AND HONORS

Section II. NON-COMBAT MEDALS AND RIBBONS

The mark of a distinctive Officer is the number of ribbons he wears on his chest. However, an Officer need not necessarily go overseas and fight in battles to look impressive. (See Figs. 14 and 15)

Front view of Lt. Col. Lester Kent, Recruiting Booth Commanding Officer outside Disneyland, who has been in service since a week ago last Friday.

Rear view of Lt. Col. Lester Kent, showing some more non-combat ribbons. Hold picture in front of X-ray machine for view of beribboned undershirt.

Here are some important decorations, citations, and service medals an ambitious Officer can earn without getting involved in battles and other distasteful and sloppy operations:

N. Y. LINCOLN AND HOLLAND TUNNELS DEFENSE SERVICE

TIMES SQUARE RECRUITING BOOTH CROSS

FORT ORD BRIDGE GAME ELIMINATION VICTORY MEDAL

U. S. ARMY KNITTING EXPERT ON RIGGED TV QUIZ CAMPAIGN

MERITORIOUS SERVICE PHILADELPHIA, PA., STARLING INVASION

DISTINGUISHED SUBWAY RIDING TO AND FROM BROOKLYN ARMY BASE

OFFICER'S CLUB DANCE AND CARD PARTY CAMPAIGN

ARMY OF OCCUPATION, BOISE, IDAHO

CHAPTER 11
THE CHAIN OF COMMAND

Section 1. HOW INFORMATION FILTERS DOWN

In today's modern Army, important information filters down through a complex, vital chain of command. For example, the President receives some Top Secret information. Here is how this information is passed on down through Army Echelons:

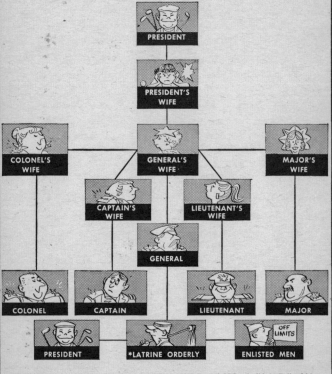

*Note importance of Latrine Orderly in Army Chain of Command. Not only did the Enlisted Men get the important information from him, he's the one who gave it to the President in the first place.

CHAPTER 16
OFFICER'S MORALE

Section 1. CHICKEN SERVICE SONGS

The Inspection Song

to the tune of "The Air Force Song"

Off we go
    Into the barracks yonder,
Pulling an
    Inspection again;
Roar right in
    Just like a clap of thunder;
Scare the hell
    Out of the men!
        Hoo-Hah! Hee!

Gig 'em all,
    This is no time to blunder,
Get K.P.'s
    Like never before;
We live to harrass
    The enlisted class,
        Hey!
Nothing can stop
    The "Chicken Brass" corps!

The Chickens Go Bucking Along
to the tune of

"The Caissons Go Rolling Along"

Buck for leaf,
    Buck for star,
A brown nose
    Will take you far,
As the "Chickens"
    Go bucking along.

Swallow pride
    Use back-pats;
You will rise
    Among brass-hats,
As the "Chickens"
    Go bucking along.

For it's buck-buck-buck,
    Hear the "Chicken Soldiers" cluck;
Raise up your voices loud and strong!
    BUCK-BUCK!

And where e'er you go,
    Always use some snow,
And you'll keep right
    On bucking along.

From The Halls Of Old R.O.T.C.

to the tune of "The Marine Corps Hymn"

From the halls of old R. O. T. C.
    To the rooms at O.C.S.
We are taught that all Enlisted Men
    Have to live in great distress.

So we badger and annoy-oy them
    With our chores both cruel and mean,
And instead of fighting ba-ttles,
    They are cleaning up latrines.

END

DON MARTIN DEPT.

Don has always been fascinated with our "Scenes We'd Like To See",

THE

1

SKREEEEE

2

so he's tried one himself. Here, then, is a Don Martin version of

CHASE

END

Today, we live in an age of specialization. Everybody is a specialist. In fact, specialization has even hit the TV series. As a result, we've got heroes who only operate in space, heroes who only operate underwater, heroes who only

HIGHWAY

You vicious criminal! You were doing 10 miles an hour. Don't you know there's a school crossing 63 miles up ahead, and you're supposed to slow down to 5!?

It'll be dark in 5 hours! How come your headlights aren't on!?

What's the idea of terrorizing decent American motorists and pedestrians with your criminal act of throwing a gum wrapper from your car!?

operate in courtrooms, heroes who only operate on farms, and, of course, all those heroes who only operate out West. But our favorite hero is the lovable guy who only operates on highways! We're talking about Lieutenant Don Mildew, of

SQUAD

All this will cost you $150. You can either sit in jail and pay the judge in three weeks— or pay us now, in small bills, so we can divide it up easier!

Hold it! Hold it! You aren't supposed to be shooting this scene, idiots! Our show is about HEROIC arrests made by our nation's Highway Squads, not about True-To-Life Highway Squad arrests! Cut to HEADQUARTERS!

ATT-89

Well, if it isn't 2150! You're 19-1040-52-11!

What he said was: Well if it isn't Don Mildew, the scourge of highway criminals! You're the only one who can capture Dennis Pivnik and make the roads safe for the little people . . . the little drivers, the little pedestrians, and mainly the little cops who hide behind billboards at speed traps!

Growl! Rowf! Sorry I can't get out of the car and give you all my autograph, but with my weight, by the time I squeeze back into the car, Pivnik would be somewhere beyond the Panama Canal.

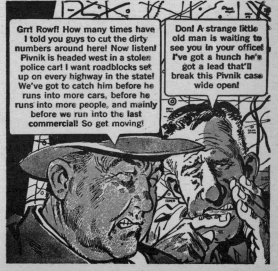

60

63

END

Did you ever stop to wonder about how recent historical events will be reported in elementary school history books 100 years from now? We hate to think so, but in the year 2060, say, elementary school history books will probably be exactly the way they are now. Which means they will be simply written so that children who study them can find easy answers for EVERYTHING, even things that college professors and historians won't fully understand. F'rinstance, every historical figure will be either good or bad, with nobody a little good and a little bad the way most people *really* are. And horrible things like wars will be minimized or dispensed with in a single clean sentence or paragraph. In other words, if it's anything like we've got today, here is how a typical elementary school American History book of the year 2060 will look . . .

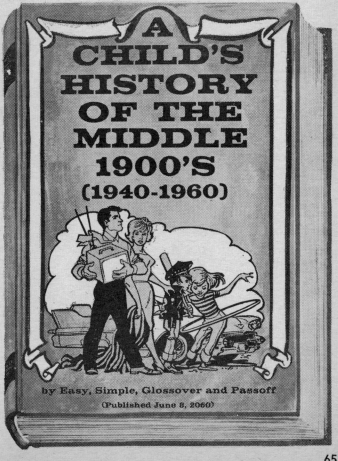

A CHILD'S HISTORY OF THE MIDDLE 1900'S (1940-1960)

by Easy, Simple, Glossover and Passoff

(Published June 8, 2060)

CHAPTER I
THE COMING OF WORLD WAR II
How the War came and how We won and how our Enemies Lost and how People were Killed and how all this resulted in Television.

In 1940, Germany had a leader named Adolph Hitler. He wanted many things for himself and his country, but he didn't like to ask for them. So he took them. The things he took were, money, valuables, other countries and other people. He put these people in all-year-round camps. He was a selfish man.

Hitler declared war on the United States and our Allies. Helping him were an Italian leader named Benito Mussolini, and a Japanese Emperor named Hirohito. Like Hitler, they were also selfish and bad. But after the war, Hirohito became good. Hitler and Mussolini also became good. Good and dead.

However, although their leaders were bad, the German people had always been good. They had never been bad. The Allies learned this after the war through the aid of post-war American Pocket Books and post-war American Motion Pictures.

These Pocket Books and Motion Pictures pointed out how good the Germans really were. The reason they were so good was because they had never liked the foolish things Hitler had done. Such as losing the war.

When peace came in 1945, America and her Allies, England, and France, were as good as they had been before the war. Our enemies, Germany, Italy and Japan, who had once been bad, became good. But our other Allies, China and Russia, who had once been good, became bad. Spain had always been bad. So had a man named Tommy Manville. But we will discuss him in a later chapter entitled "20th Century Hobbies".

In 1950, there was a War in Korea. However, since television was already here at the time, most people paid little attention to it. We will discuss television in a later chapter. The Korean War was bad.

Here we see Adolph Hitler and his Nazi followers at a crowded political meeting in a Munich beer hall. This meeting was known as the "Beer Hall Putsch" because it was so crowded, everybody kept putsching and tschoving. The picture shows clearly what a selfish man Hitler was. Note how much bigger his glass is than the others.

CHAPTER II
LIFE IN THE MIDDLE 1900'S
How we couldn't get Peace and how we couldn't get Disarmament and how we couldn't get a Man into Space and how we got Payola

Life in general was quite good in this era. Many Americans bought autos, homes, washers, dryers, and air conditioners on credit. But the only ones who could buy these things on credit were those who had once bought *other* things on credit, and who could thus prove what good credit risks they were. Poorest credit risks were those people with so much money that they had never bought anything on credit before, and who thus couldn't prove what good credit risks they *could be.*

Poorest credit risk in the United States at that time was a prominent family named Rockefeller.

All this was very confusing, especially to the Russians. Most Russians didn't have this problem. Most Russians also didn't have autos, homes, washers, dryers, and air conditioners. What they did have was a Communist-type H-Bomb, which was bad. We had a Democratic-type H-Bomb, which was good.

We will now discuss the difference between Democracy and Communism.

American Democracy worked like this: if a man had a cow, he kept it, milked it, sold part of the milk, and drank the rest himself. Then, he butchered the cow, sold part of it, and ate the rest of the meat himself.

Russian Communism worked like this: if a man had a cow, the *State* kept it, the *State* milked it, and the man drank vodka. Then the *State* butchered the cow and divided it up equally among the people for food. The man got back the tail to eat, so he drank more vodka.

Chinese Communism worked like this: if a man had a cow, he turned it in to the State as subversive, along with his wife and children. Then the State butchered his family, and the man ate and drank nothing.

There was also a lot of nuclear testing in those days, and people were scared that the end of the world was coming. That was bad. Except that there were also Diner's Club Cards in those days, and people were living it up even if they couldn't afford it. That was good. Because it sort of evened things up.

Here is a typical American home, circa 1960. The man in the picture has bought everything you see on credit, with the exception of the object on the extreme right. That object is a "wife".

CHAPTER III
THE GLORIOUS ERA OF ENTERTAINMENT

How we Survived the Deadly H-Bomb so that we could enjoy Television and Rock 'n Roll and Horror Movies and how it Probably wasn't Worth It

In the late 1940's, a phenomenon called television (or TV) came into the American home. In some ways it was good, and in some ways it was awful. In fact, that was what many people said at the time, "Television is good and awful!"

On TV, a man named Milton Berle was good. Soon he became bad. A man named Ed Sullivan was bad. Soon he became worse. This made him good. A man named Sid Caesar was good. Soon he became better. This made him bad. A few Westerns and Private-Eye shows were good, but most were bad. The good ones stayed on. So did the bad ones. Situation Comedies were so bad, they were good. In fact, they were so funny, even some dead people laughed at them. On records and tape.

In 1959, there were TV scandals. They were bad for a very important moral reason. The people involved got caught.

All this led to a complete overhauling of television by fearless and progressive TV network executives. Two important decisions were reached.

The two CLEAN-OUR-OWN-TV-HOUSE decisions:

Here is a picture of an historical TV figure. His name was Mr. Charles Van Doren, and he was very good. He was very good at answering questions. He was also very good at memorizing the answers to these questions which TV producers gave him in advance. Before they caught him, many fine Congressmen liked to say, "God bless you!" to him, although he hardly ever sneezed.

(1) From that time on, whenever possible, no two Westerns would follow each other on the same channel. Instead, a Private-Eye show would be inserted between them. This decision is now known in TV history as "More Balanced Programming".

(2) Additional TV shows would be added to each channel. These shows would be educational as well as entertaining, and would deal with men with bigger guns and harder blackjacks and sharper knives who offered their service to the public. This decision is now known in TV history as "More Public Service Shows".

At that time, there was an organization called the F.C.C. Its job was to regulate TV for the good of the people. What it did was indeed good for the people. The people who ran N.B.C., the people who ran C.B.S., and the people who ran A.B.C. This decision is now known in TV history as "More Highway Robbery".

Other forms of entertainment in those days were "Rock 'n Roll" and "Horror Movies". These will be discussed in a later chapter entitled "The End of Civilization As We Once Knew It."

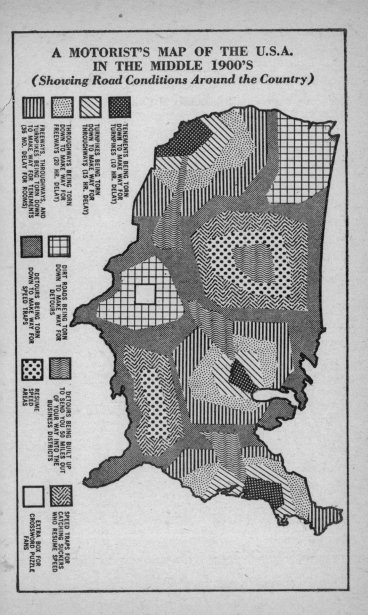

A MOTORIST'S MAP OF THE U.S.A.
IN THE MIDDLE 1900'S
(Showing Road Conditions Around the Country)

TENEMENTS BEING TORN DOWN TO MAKE WAY FOR TURNPIKES (110 HR. DELAY)

TURNPIKES BEING TORN DOWN TO MAKE WAY FOR THROUGHWAYS (15 HR. DELAY)

THROUGHWAYS BEING TORN DOWN TO MAKE WAY FOR FREEWAYS (20 HR. DELAY)

FREEWAYS, THROUGHWAYS, AND TURNPIKES BEING TORN DOWN TO MAKE WAY FOR TENEMENTS (36 MO. DELAY FOR ROOMS)

DIRT ROADS BEING TORN DOWN TO MAKE WAY FOR DETOURS

DETOURS BEING TORN DOWN TO MAKE WAY FOR SPEED TRAPS

DETOURS BEING BUILT UP TO SEND YOU 50 MILES OUT OF YOUR WAY INTO THE BUSINESS DISTRICTS

RESUME SPEED AREAS

SPEED TRAPS FOR CATCHING SUCKERS WHO RESUME SPEED

EXTRA BOX FOR CROSSWORD PUZZLE FANS

69

CHAPTER IV
AMERICAN PRESIDENTS OF THE MIDDLE 1900's

FRANKLIN D. ROOSEVELT
Term of Office: 1932-1945

America's 32nd President was a man named Franklin D. Roosevelt. Most people thought he was a good man. However, a newspaper columnist named Westbrook Pegler thought he was a bad man. Pegler thought Roosevelt helped start long, cruel World War II. Pegler wanted Roosevelt to be as good as Pegler's employer, William Randolph Hearst, had been. After all, William Randolph Hearst had never helped start long, cruel wars like World War II. He had only helped start short, funny wars like the Spanish-American War. Roosevelt was famous for saying: "I hate war!" Pegler was famous for saying: "I hate Roosevelt!" Hearst was famous for saying: "I love money!"

Franklin D. Roosevelt's first term was an initial success

President Harry S. Truman at the piano, and his daughter, Margaret at the microphone, entertaining at a Democratic Party fund-raising dinner. This performance helped raise over $150,000 in campaign funds — for the Republican Party.

HARRY S. TRUMAN
Term of Office: 1945-1952

America's 33rd President was a man named Harry S. Truman. Truman helped start his own war. It was more terrible than both World War I and World War II combined. It was his war with the music critics concerning Truman's daughter Margaret's singing voice. In spite of their criticism, Margaret soon began to sing all over the country. This was a brilliant victory for Truman. This was a terrible defeat for the Music World.

Truman also helped start the Korean War which was discussed in great length in the last line of Chaper I.

Truman was famous for saying: "#&$#@°¢†#&!"

THOMAS E. DEWEY
Term of Office: 1948—?

Thomas E. Dewey, a former New York District Attorney, was elected to the Presidency in 1948. However, for some reason, all records of Dewey's term of office are destroyed or missing, and very little is known about his years in the White House. Interested students may find more details of his election in the following two books: "The Collected Headlines of the 1948 Chicago Tribune" and "The Best of H. V. Kaltenborn's Election Night Radio and Television Speeches".

Dewey was famous for saying: "Hey, what happened?"

President-Elect Thomas E. Dewey (with broom) spelling regular Republican Headquarters Janitor, Alfred M. Landon, immediately after the 1948 election results had come in.

DWIGHT D. EISENHOWER
Term of Office: 1952-1960

Dwight D. Eisenhower, America's 34th President, was a very very good man. Everybody loved him. He was elected President in November, 1952. He was inaugurated in January, 1953. And he took over his duties of office in June, 1959, following the death of John Foster Dulles.

Eisenhower was famous for saying: "Well, now, if we are to look at the overall picture, that is to say, in regard to that question, which of course, I haven't, to any degree, as yet studied or read up on, I would say, in all probability, emphatically, I think so."

Interested students may find additional information on famous Eisenhower speeches in the book, "The Collected Press Conference Statements of Dwight D. Eisenhower, as translated by Casey Stengel".

President Eisenhower during one of his press conferences, telling newspapermen why he is strongly against children making bets on horses. This is an example of his typical, hard-hitting statements on the troublesome race problem.

CHAPTER V
MEDICAL SCIENCE IN THE MIDDLE 1900's

How Medical Men Saved us from Deadly Scourges which might never have existed if Nature had been Kinder and if Madison Ave. Ad Agencies hadn't Made Them Up in the first place.

THE EVIL OF THE "A'S"

The "A's" were vicious elements which had a deadly habit of failing to push open stomach trap doors fast enough. Their lazy, slow movement into the bloodstream caused 20th Century Man untold misery in the forms of upset stomachs. But thanks to Medical Science's eager and swift elements ... called "B's", stomach trap doors were opened much faster, and no more stomachs were upset. Except those belonging to people who had seen too many "A" and "B" races on TV.

THE HORRORS OF THE YELLOW

The yellow was an ugly-colored mass which made its home on the surface of 20th Century Man's teeth. People were advised that if they fought this scourge with a medical miracle called Pepsident, they would wonder where the yellow went. Those who did, found out: in a straight line down the middle of their backs for not having the courage to report Pepsident to the Unfair Advertising Practices Committee.

THE TERROR OF "BRAND X"

"Brand X" was a bad 20th Century product which caused a great deal of mental anguish to anyone who came in contact with it. Unfortunately, Medical Science could never wipe it out. Because the new good product it would develop for one ad agency, which was better than "Brand X", would turn out to be another ad agency's "Brand X", and the first "Brand X" would turn out to be this other ad agency's new good product, which also had been developed by Medical Science. Students disturbed and confused by all this should read the book: "The Rover Boys at Uncle Randolph's Farm". You won't learn anything new but it might help you forget.

THE THREAT OF CANCER

Cancer was an annoying thing which bothered 20th Century Man at times. However, since Medical Science was already occupied with the battle against really important evils (see above examples), not very much was done about it. But in all fairness, it should be pointed out that, because they paid close attention to what ad agencies said, people put to permanent rest by cancer were rarely troubled by halitosis, tired blood, five o'clock shadow, excess fat, etc.

FURTHER READINGS

Here is a partial list of books which will afford the student further enlightenment on the subjects already fully covered in previous chapters, so you really don't have to bother reading them: "HOW HITLER COULD HAVE PUT SOME FUN IN HIS LIFE IF HE'D TRIED DANCING", by Kathryn Murray; "WE ARE LOSING THE U.S.S.R. TO THE RUSSIANS", by Rep. Francis Walters; "WHAT EVER HAPPENED TO ELOISE MacELHONE AND OTHER TV HAS-BEENS?", by Jerry Lester; "TRUCK DRIVERS WHOSE TOES GET STEPPED ON SAY THE DARNDEST THINGS", by Art Linkletter; "HOW I ALMOST MADE THE ARMY MY CAREER IF IT WASN'T FOR THE MONEY", by Elvis Presley.

TEST YOURSELF

1. Why would Nikita Khrushchev have made a poor blind date?
2. What was Lawrence Welk trying to say?
3. Could there have been peace in those times without Tuesday Weld?
4. How much do you know about the Mafia?
5. Where do you want your body sent?

SUGGESTIONS AND PROJECTS

1. In the following space, write down all the things you can think of about television which helped to educate and uplift 20th Century Man.

* * * *

2. Draw a map of Jersey City in the middle 1900's. Color the street areas in red, the park areas in green, the house areas in blue, the shopping areas in yellow, and the historical landmarks in purple. Include lines of longitude and latitude, and a precise scale of miles. Show this map to your teacher. She'll think it's a stupid idea.

* * * *

3. Pretend you are a 20th Century advertising man. Pretend you have to write an ad telling about the evils of "Tired Blood". Go to the library and find some real middle 1900 ads about "Tired Blood". Pretend you have written these ads, and show them to your parents. They'll have you committed to an insane asylum. *They* won't be pretending.

* * * *

4. Take a drive to the seashore to go bathing. Stop when you get caught in the traffic jam. Look at the other cars around you. Notice that many of them are 1960 models. These cars left for the beach 100 years ago, and still haven't made it. In 1960, this was called "Traffic medium to heavy".

* * * *

5. Contact as many school principals as you can, and tell them how wonderful this history book is for pupils, and how dangerous more complete history books could be. Make them go out and buy huge quantities of this book right away. Tell them supplies are limited. This will help keep our profits high. This will help keep your intelligence low. And mainly, this will help keep everybody from progressing beyond 20th Century Man.

END

With so many industries and professions be-
moaning the fact that new, young replace-
ments are not coming along fast enough,
MAD wonders why them trading cards, collected by kids, continue to glamorize Big
League Baseball, Motion Pictures, and similar
industries that are already overcrowded.
And so, to get the kids interested in more
profitable and productive occupations early
in life, here are some samplings of our new
line of . . .

MAD
BUBBLE GUM
CARDS

BIG LEAGUE ACCOUNTING STARS No. 26

Big League Accounting Star #26

Ewald "Red Ink" Wierhoffer

Adds left handed. Subtracts right handed. Born: Teaneck, N. J., 1921. Broke into Organized Accounting in 1946 with Price Waterhouse. Traded to the Bureau of Internal Revenue, 1948. Obtained on waivers by Dow-Jones, 1954. Current salary: $12,000, plus all the petty cash he can manage to steal.

A MAD Bubble Gum Card
SAVE THE CARD—CHEW THE GUM

BIG LEAGUE ACCOUNTING STARS No. 38

Big League Accounting Star #38

Clyde "Unbalanced" Reeber

Set all-time record in 1955, juggling five sets of books for Potrzebie Trucking Company, which was a front for a Hot Car Ring, which was a front for a Syndicate of Hired Killers, which was a front for a Neighborhood Mah Jongg Club. Signed for 20 seasons at Sing Sing. Elected to "Crooked Accounting Hall of Fame," 1953.

A MAD Bubble Gum Card
CHEW THE CARD—SAVE THE GUM

FAMOUS PHYSICIANS

No. 18

Famous Physician #18

Dr. Boris "All Thumbs" Acid

Signed up by Angel of Mercy Hospital, Knoxville, Montana, 1947. Performed first $400 appendectomy, 1949. Tried out as Brain Surgeon, 1950, and failed. Beat five malpractice suits in one season, 1954. Currently first-string Gall Bladder man at Cedars of Beverly Hills Hospital, Lebanon, Va.

A MAD Bubble Gum Card
SAVE THE GUM—THROW AWAY THE CARD

WORLD'S GREAT TEACHERS

No. 35

World's Great Teacher #35

Walter "Botchy" Smitner

Elected as "Most Popular Teacher" by students of North Fork, Iowa, High School, 1955, after chemistry experiment he was performing blew up North Fork, Iowa, High School. Also well-loved by pupils for neglecting to take attendance 126 consecutive days, and forgetting to give final exams for 14 consecutive semesters.

A MAD Bubble Gum Card
SAVE WRAPPER—THROW AWAY GUM AND CARD

Famous Physician #51

Dr. Herman Witheringpuss

First doctor in medical history to specialize in TV Commercials. Hit big time by becoming one of five leading New York doctors to recommend Carter's Little Liver Pills, 1951. Acquainted public with discovery of little trap door in stomach, 1955. Pointed out how concentrated stomach acid can burn a hole in a napkin to 32,000,000 viewers, 1959. Now playing with Congressional Committee Investigating Fraudulent Television Advertising.

A MAD Bubble Gum Card
SAVE GUM AND CARD—THROW AWAY WRAPPER

World's Great Teacher #22

Rosemary "Battleaxe" Winecoop

Now in her 52nd year as fourth grade teacher at P. S. 86, Indianapolis, Mo. Holds lifetime record for teaching young clods to sing "America the Beautiful": 3,127. Boasts .317 lifetime average for bringing cry of pain by swatting knuckles with rulers. Voted "Most Sullen Playground Monitor", in 1928, 1929, 1933, 1937, 1952 and '53.

A MAD Bubble Gum Card
SAVE THE CARD—THROW AWAY THE GUM

OUTSTANDING TREE SURGEONS

No. 7

Outstanding Tree Surgeon #7

Carlyle F. Burnlash

First Tree Surgeon to discover that Pepsi-Cola, injected into roots of young saplings, would prevent Chestnut Blight and produce young, fair and debonair bark. Believed to be the only Tree Surgeon in U. S. who refuses to make house calls. Author of standard reference work, "What To Do Until The Tent Caterpillars Come".

A MAD Bubble Gum Card.
CHEW WRAPPER—SAVE CARD—THROW AWAY GUM

GLAMOROUS STOCKBROKERS

No. 6

Glamorous Stockbroker #6

Merrill Lynch Piercefenner

With his wife as dummy Board Member, set up fraudulent Brokerage Firm of Merrill Lynch Piercefenner and Gladys, 1950. Sold 500,000 shares of Pierce-Arrow Auto stock, 1951, after spreading rumor that company had merely shut down for re-tooling in 1935. Went bankrupt in 1957, purchasing 450,000 shares of Pierce-Arrow Auto stock, after forgetting who started the rumor.

A MAD Bubble Gum Card
CHEW WHOLE MESS—THROW UP EVERYTHING

OUTSTANDING TREE SURGEONS

No. 19

Outstanding Tree Surgeon #19

Enoch Saltzpritcher

Only Tree Surgeon east of the Mississippi to be charged with Malpractice. Set up notorious Saltzspritcher Clinic, in 1947, claiming to cure Dutch Elm disease with electric box emitting thought waves. Conducted experiments aimed at curing depression among Weeping Willows through psychoanalysis, 1952. Deported to Black Forest, in Germany, season of 1952.

A MAD Bubble Gum Card
CHEW WRAPPER—SAVE GUM—THROW AWAY CARD

GLAMOROUS STOCKBROKERS

No. 29

Glamorous Stockbroker #29

Getyer "Cotten Picken'" Hanzoff

Made $3,000,000 in 1949 by cornering Cotton Market. Lost $3,000,000 in 1950 after worst boll weevil epidemic in 40 years. Recouped fortune in 1951 by discovering how to make Automobile Tires out of boll weevils. Lost fortune in 1952, after specializing in manufacturing tires for expected Pierce-Arrow Autos.

A MAD Bubble Gum Card
SAVE STOMACH—DON'T EAT THIS JUNK

FANTASTIC SCIENTISTS

No. 4

Fantastic Scientist #4

Dr. Neville Sternbrush

Won fame for being the world's first scientist to apply discoveries in Advanced Physics to problems in everyday life. Disintegrated his landlord, 1948. Put his wife into orbit, 1951. Planted his mother-in-law on dark side of moon, 1955. Dr. Sternbrush disappeared completely in 1957.

A MAD Bubble Gum Card
SAVE JUNK—EARN MONEY TO BUY EATS

NOTORIOUS AUTO MECHANICS

No. 33

Notorious Auto Mechanic #33

Rudy "The Padder" Gougewell

Often called the "Noah Webster" of the Auto Repair industry for inventing technical terms that put all repair discussions beyond the grasp of laymen. Became first mechanic to bill a customer for Resetting Gummage, 1946. Popularized 1,000-mile Ampere Check-Up and Replacement, 1949. Advocated Annual Rotation of Drive Shaft Nilds, 1954. Retired as millionaire, 1957

A MAD Bubble Gum Card
SAVE NOTHING—THROW AWAY WHOLE MESS

FANTASTIC SCIENTISTS

No. 37

Seymour "Microfilm" Verblanger

Became the nation's first millionaire scientist by stealing American Atomic Secrets and selling them to Russia, and while doing so, stealing Russian Atomic Secrets and selling them to the Americans. Now playing in Latin America, selling Nicaraguan Atomic Secrets to Costa Rica and Guatemalan Atomic Secrets to El Salvador, which is a pretty neat trick, since Nicaragua and Guatemala don't have any Atomic Secrets to begin with.

A MAD Bubble Gum Card
WE'VE RUN OUT OF VARIATIONS ON THIS GAG

NOTORIOUS AUTO MECHANICS

No. 41

Omar "Sparky" Wintermutt

First Auto Mechanic in history to invent method for tuning an engine so badly that the damage could only be undone by a $400 Complete Overhaul. Invented Indelible Grease for wiping on steering wheels, 1951. Developed foolproof method for replacing spark plugs with very same spark plugs, 1952. Elected to "Disreputable Auto Mechanics Hall of Fame", 1953.

A MAD Bubble Gum Card
SAVE MONEY—DON'T BUY THIS JUNK

HOT SHOT POLITICIANS	No. 79	Hotshot Politician #79

John Ward Heeler, Jr.

Became first politician in 100 years to take novel approach to campaigning, by coming out: against Motherhood, in 1929; against Home and Family, 1933; against The Flag, 1938; against Our Boys in Uniform, 1942; against Lower Taxes, 1950. Also became first politician of modern times to complete entire career without ever being nominated for anything.

A MAD Bubble Gum Card
AND THE LAST ONE—THANK GOODNESS!

END

In 1888, some "square" named Ernest Lawrence Thayer wrote a poem which was destined for wide acclaim, entitled "Casey at the Bat." But, like all poems of that period, it was written in the language of that period (which figures!) To bring it up to date, MAD presents a "hip" version of the poem which is destined for obscurity, entitled:

"COOL" CASEY AT THE BAT

The action wasn't groovy for the Endsville nine that days.
The beat was 4 to 2 with just one chorus more to sway.

And when old Cooney conked at first, and Barrows also sacked,
A nowhere rumble bugged up all the cats who dug the act.

A hassled group got all hung up and started in to split;
The other cats there played it cool and stayed to check the bit:
They figured if old Casey could, like, get in one more lick—
We'd put a lot of bread down, Man, on Casey and his stick!

85

But Flynn swung before Casey, and also Cornball Blake,
And the first stud didn't make it, and the other couldn't fake;
So the cats and all their chicks were dragged and in a bluesy groove,
For it was a sucker's long-shot that old Casey'd make his move.

But Flynn blew one cool single, and the hipsters did a flip,
And Blake, who was a loser, gave the old ball quite a trip;
And when the tempo let up, like a chorus played by Bird,
There was Cornball stashed at second and Flynn holed up at third.

Then from five thousand stomping cats there came a crazy sound;
It rocked all through the scene, Man — it really rolled around;
It went right to the top, Dad, and it charged on down below,
For Casey, swinging Casey — he was comin' on to blow!

There was style in Casey's shuffle as he came on with his stick;
There was jive in Casey's strutting; he was on a happy kick.
And when, to clue in all the cats, he doffed his lid real big,
The Square Johns in the group were hip: t'was Casey on the gig.

Ten thousand peepers piped him as he rubbed fuzz on his palms;
Five thousand choppers grooved it when he smeared some on his arms.
Then while the shook-up pitcher twirled the ball snagged in his clutch,
A hip look lit up Casey, Man, this cat was just too much!

And now the crazy mixed-up ball went flying out through space.
But Casey, he just eyed it with a cool look on his face.
Right at that charged-up sideman, the old ball really sailed —
"That's too far out," sang Casey. "Like, Strike One!" the umpire wailed.

From the pads stacked high with hipsters there was heard a frantic roar,
Like the beating of the bongos from a frenzied Be-Bop score,
"Knife him! Knife that ump, Man!" wailed some weirdo left-field clown;
And they would have cut the cat up, but cool Casey put them down.

With a real gone Beatnik grin on him, old Casey cooked with gas;
He fanned down all that ribble, and he sang, "On with this jazz!"
He set the pitcher straight, and once again the old ball flew;
But Casey wouldn't buy it and the ump howled, "Like, Strike Two!"

"He's sick!" wailed all the hipsters, and the Squares, too, sang out "Sick!"
But a nod from Daddy Casey, and those cats got off that kick.
They dug the way he sizzled, like his gaskets were of wax;
They were hip that Casey wouldn't let the ball get by his ax.

The cool look's gone from Casey's chops, his eyes are all popped up;
He stomps his big ax on the plate, he really is hopped up.

And now the pitcher cops the ball, and now it comes on fast,
And now the joint is jumpin' with the sound of Casey's blast.

Man, somewhere in this far-out scene the sun is packing heat;
The group is blowing somewhere, and somewhere guts are beat,

And somewhere big cats break up, and small cats raise the roof;
But there is no joy in Endsville — Swinging Casey made a goof.

END

Recently, some smart producer got the bright idea to make a musical out of "Li'l Abner!", and it turned out to be a resounding success both on Broadway, and as a Hollywood movie. The way we look at it, this will probably start a whole rash of musicals based on comic strips, like "Kerry Get Your Gun", "Call Me Sluggo" and "The Little King and I". So, to nip this nauseating trend in the bud, here is our version of a comic strip musical to end all comic strip musicals . . . mainly . . .

The Mad "Comic" Opera

ACT 1, SCENE 1:
THE OFFICE OF DICK TRACY

Sung to the tune of "September Song"

ACT 1, SCENE 2: DUGAN'S BAR

*Sung to the tune of "I Get A Kick Out Of You"

*Sung to the tune of "Old Man River"

ACT 1, SCENE 3; IN A PLANE, 18,000 FEET UP

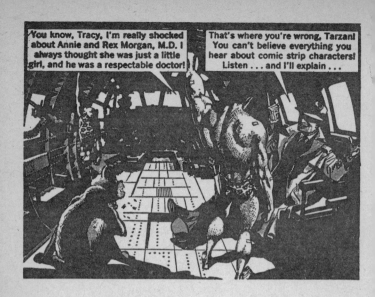

Sung to the tune of "Swanee"

113

THE END

Ingredients: Roasted Peanuts, Sugar, Corn Syrup, Vegetable Oil, Powdered Skim Milk, Cocoa, Salt, Pure Food Starch, Emulsifier, Assorted Mouse Droppings, Factory Dust, Dandruff, Belly-Button Lint, Artificial Flavor, Artificial Color, and Artificial Candy

WHAT'S IN IT FOR ME DEPT.

Did you ever notice how they always print the ingredients of a candy or food or drug on the label or wrapper? This practice is required by the "Pure Food and Drugs Act" which was passed so instead of worrying about what kind of awful slop you're swallowing, you know exactly what kind of awful slop you're swallowing. Actually, this business of listing the contents of a can of food or bottle of drugs or box of candy is a good idea. But, in order to fully protect the American consumer, we think this practice should be extended to other areas besides food and drugs. In other words, we think Congress should immediately pass

MAD'S
"PURE PRODUCTS" LAW

UNDER MAD'S "PURE PRODUCTS" LAW, A LIST OF INGREDIENTS WOULD BE REQUIRED ON EVERYTHING, LIKE F'RINSTANCE . . .

CARS

INGREDIENTS: Shatterproof Glass, Shatterprone Plastic, Thin-Gauge American Steel, Inferior German and Japanese Steel, Molded Cardboard, Synthetic Rubber, Faulty Welding, Loose Nuts and Bolts, Leaks, Squeaks, Rattles, Groans, Whines, Womens, Songs, Microscopic Chromium Plating, Fastenings of Thumb Tacks, Scotch Tape, Glue and Spit, and Exorbitant Finance Rates with Carrying Charges.

TAKE A DEMONSTRATION RIDE IN THE GREAT NEW
BELCHFIRE-8
THEN WHEN YOU BUY IT, YOU'LL REALLY BE TAKEN FOR A RIDE!

MEN'S SUITS

BROOKS BROTHER in-law
HARRY

INGREDIENTS: 45% Re-Processed Yak Hair, 41% Re-Claimed Lemur Wool, 12% Excelsior, 2% Brillo, Salvaged Thread, Irritating Dyes, Imitation Cloth Linings, Imitation Bone Buttons and Imitation Fancy Label.

119

NEWSPAPERS

INGREDIENTS: Wood Pulp Paper, Smeary Ink, Crossword Puzzles, Comics, Unreliable Weather Reports, Dishonest Advertisements, Sensational Headlines, Biased Editorials, Atrocious Grammar, Assorted Libels, Misprints, Misspellings, and Mistaken Facts with Artificial Local Coloring Added to Increase Circulation.

INGREDIENTS: Warped Doors and Floors, Faulty Plumbing, Insufficient Insulation, Inadequate Wiring, Electrical Fixtures Imported From Outer Mongolia, Simulated-Wood Wallpaper, Simulated-Wood Cabinets, Simulated-Wood Wood, Cardboard Roofing Shingles, Paper Maché Bricks, Pressed-Sand Cement, Celluloid Bathroom Tiles, Leaks, Creaks, Termites, Heavy Mortgage Rates, and High Tax Assessments.

BUY A

SHLOCK CHALET

ONLY

$14,990

DOWN

Wall-To-Wall Carpeting
and
Back-To-Wall Payments

CIGARETTES

INGREDIENTS: 1% High-Grade Tobacco, 2½% Average-Grade Tobacco, 49% Rotten-Grade Tobacco, 40% Chopped Tobacco Stems, 7% Other Assorted Plant Leaves, Artificial Flavor, Cigarette Paper Made From Old Rags, Filter Paper Made From Old Cigarette Paper, Nicotine, Tars, and Deadly Throat and Lung Irritants

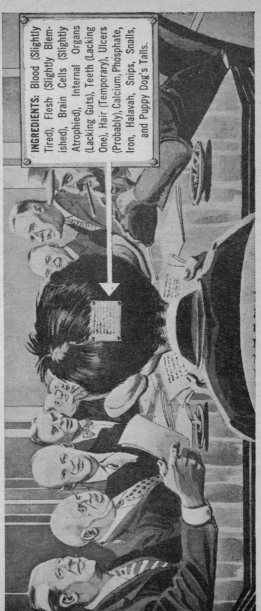

INGREDIENTS: Blood (Slightly Tired), Flesh (Slightly Blemished), Brain Cells (Slightly Atrophied), Internal Organs (Lacking Guts), Teeth (Lacking One), Hair (Temporary), Ulcers (Probably), Calcium, Phosphate, Iron, Halavah, Snips, Snails, and Puppy Dog's Tails.

Since doing an article (MAD #41) in which Power Boating was the main topic, we have been deluged by requests to give equal time to another popular form of boating—namely, Sailboating. For example, J. Flushing Head, President of *Exclusive Yacht Clubs of America*, writes: "It is true that Power Boat owners

SAIL

MAIN DIFFERENCE BETWEEN A POWER

Power boat owner is usually dressed in a sparkling gay sports ensemble following an unpretentious nautical motif

have the feeling their crafts are speedy, dependable, comfortable, safe, and have resale value . . . but there is one feeling they can never have—the feeling every Sailboat owner cherishes—mainly, that deep sense of being better than anybody else!" MAD now sets the record straight with

ING

BOAT OWNER AND A SAILBOAT OWNER

Sailboat owner is usually dressed in a soaking wet sports ensemble following an unforeseen change in the wind

METHODS OF THE TYPES

There are two methods of distinguishing the many types of sailboats. One is by

COMMON SAILBOAT HULLS

Sloop Hull

Yawl Hull

RECOGNIZING OF SAILBOATS

the shape of the hull, and the other is by the rigging of the sails.

Ketch Hull

Rotten Hull

COMMON SAILBOAT RIGGING

Sloop Rigging

Yawl Rigging

Ketch Rigging

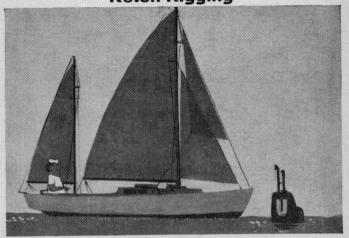

Cheap Rigging

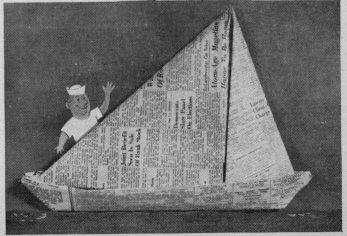

BECOMING FAMILIAR WITH

If one is to take up Sailing, the first lesson one should learn is to become familiar with the equipment necessary to thoroughly enjoy this sport. Study the diagram below

(1) Mainsail
(2) Jib
(3) Backstay
(4) Jibstay
(5) Leech
(6) Upper Shroud
(7) Lower Shroud
(8) Boom Vang
(9) Jumper Stay
(10) Jumper Strut
(11) Tiller
(12) Rudder
(13) Keel
(14) Clew

(15) Foot
(16) Tack
(17) Miter Seam
(18) Cockpit
(19) Deck
(20) Topside
(21) Mainmast
(22) Mended Mainmast

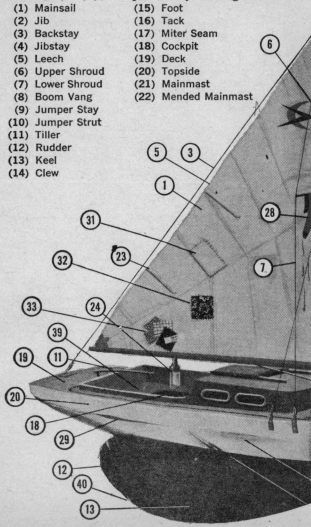

NECESSARY SAILING EQUIPMENT

carefully, and you will have learned this first lesson.
You will also have learned a second lesson: mainly not
to get too familiar with that other necessary equipment!

(23) Batten
(24) Bourbon
(25) Chine
(26) Dry Rot
(27) Dry Sock
(28) Wet Sock
(29) Crack
(30) Hole

(31) Matched Patch
(32) Mismatched Patch
(33) Mish-mosh Patch
(34) Orange Peelings
(35) Paint Peelings
(36) Squashed Sandwich
(37) Scrape
(38) Smear
(39) Splinter
(40) Split
(41) Swing
(42) Smack
(43) Other necessary
     Equipment

MAKING SURE THAT SAILING

NOT "SHIP-SHAPE"

In other words, to make sure your sailing equip.

TUNING

Since sailing is such an exacting combination of science and skill, it is important to have everything aboard as near perfect as possible. This is especially true when it comes to setting the mast. Even a frac-

When stays are loose, the result may be a cockeyed or wobbly mast.

EQUIPMENT IS "SHIP-SHAPE"

"SHIP-SHAPE"

ment has a "ship-shape", make her go on a diet!

THE MAST

tion of an inch deviation can throw the entire boat
and its performance off-balance. The mast is held
in place by stays which can be adjusted by tighten-
ing or loosening turnbuckles.

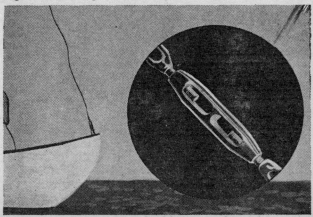

Turnbuckles are used to tighten stays.

TIGHTENING THE STAYS TO TUNE THE MAST

First, tighten jibstay turnbuckle **(A)**
This will bring mast slightly forward.

Next, tighten backstay turnbuckle **(B)**.
This will bring mast back up straight.

Next, tighten port shroud turnbuckle
(C). This will tilt mast over to port.

Now tighten starb'd shroud turnbuckle
(D). This will straighten mast again.

Now go back and tighten up (A) and (B) because they seem to have loosened up.

This will probably cause (C) and (D) to loosen, so they must be tightened.

Which will probably loosen (**A**) and (**B**)
again, so tighten them . . . which will
probably loosen (**C**) and (**D**) again, so
go back and tighten them once more . . .

Finally, you'll get to a point where
everything is almost perfect! But—
almost perfect is not good enough in
Sailing. One more turn should do it!

There! That's ... OOOOPS!

WHAT TO DO ABOUT
MAST HOLES IN A HULL

The first thing to do when a mast has been forced through a hull by one-too-many turns on a turnbuckle is to inspect the damage. Take a good look at the size of the hole, then get a length of board, and give it a quick coat of white paint. When it has dried, letter the words "For Sale" on it—and hang from the highest point on the exposed mast!

BASIC SAILING

The following are some Basic Sailing Maneuvers.
Once these basic maneuvers are mastered, the Sail-

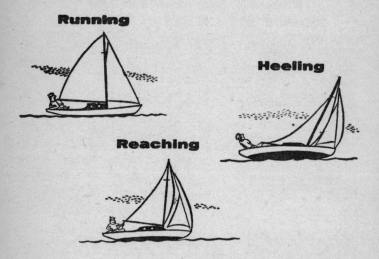

Running

Heeling

Reaching

HIKING

When a Sailboat heels (tilts to one side from the
force of the wind), it is often necessary to counter-

The above clearly illustrates the danger of "Hiking"

MANEUVERS

ing enthusiast can go almost anywhere confidently. (Safely, no . . . but confidently, yes!)

Capsizing

Sinking

Hollering

balance the effect. This is made possible by thrilling maneuver known as "Hiking."

BACK TO 0 MPH
WIND AGAIN

when the wind suddenly stops dead...

TACKING

It is not possible to sail directly into the wind, but an experienced Sailboat owner can overcome this difficulty by resorting to a maneuver known as "Tacking." By adopting a zig-zag course, heading into the wind at 45° angles, excellent progress can be made. However, great skill is required to control the boat in a strong wind. Here is an example of Tacking*...

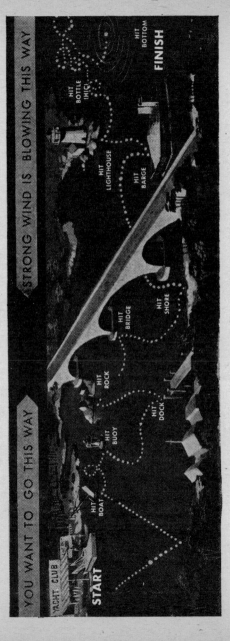

* We didn't say "a GOOD Example!"

COMMANDING THE SAILBOAT CREW

Anyone who is lucky enough to be allowed to help out on a Sailboat is technically known as "The Crew." The following is a typical example of how a Sailboat Captain commands his crew.

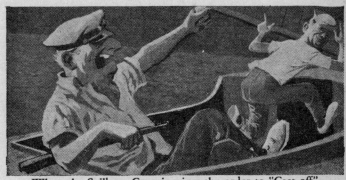

When the Sailboat Captain gives the order to "Cast off", the cruise is officially under way. The Crew immediately rushes to carry out the order, and all subsequent orders.

At the command of "Hoist the mains'l!", the crew grasps a halyard and jibbets the mainstay. He then lowers the gorsline, tightens up on the leech, and fastens the retch.

At the command of "Hoist the jib!", the crew belays the boom vang and makes fast all shrouds leading to the deck. He then stows the rinklar gear, and fastens all battens.

At the command of "Sail Ho!", he breaks out the spinnaker. If it's a Genoa rig, he fastens the stay pole to the cam crotch. He then checks for crinks and tightens all bluks.

At the command of "Ease the jib!", the crew runs forward and buffets the sheet. He quickly follows this with the familiar "Poop de deck!". He then scrubs down the deck.

At the command of "Lower the mains'l!", the crew breathes a sigh of relief, for this command means that the cruise is almost over, and he can rest his weary bones at last.

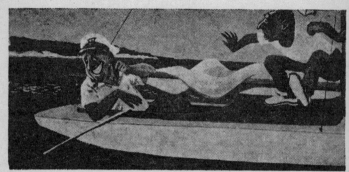

At the command of "Hoist the anchor!", the crew explodes in purple rage, for it means the Captain forgot this most important *first* command, and voyage hasn't even started!

At the command of "Awrrrrk!", the crew relaxes with the realization that the Captain is through, and the Sailboat is his. He then sets sail for South America, and freedom.

SAILING HAZARDS

As you have seen, Sailing can be a lot of fun. But if one doesn't know exactly what to watch out for, it can be pretty dangerous! (Especially if you don't happen to own a Sailboat!)

ADVERSE WIND CONDITIONS

Too Much Wind

Not Enough Wind

SUDDEN WIND SHIFTS

Wind Blowing East

Wind Shifting West

NAVIGATION LAWS
SAILBOATS HAVE THE RIGHT OF WAY

Because Sailboats cannot shift direction or change speed as easily as Power Boats, they have the right of way, and all others regardless of size, must alter their course when approaching.

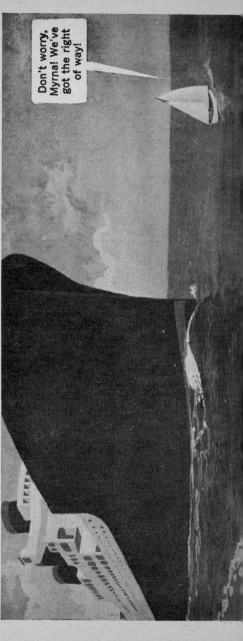

Don Martin, who gave his *awl* to illustrating our "hip" version of "Casey", now *adze* his *hone* contribution to the festivities: a *bit* of *plane* nonsense that he *a-sledges* he *hack-tually-saw* happen to

THE CARPENTER'S ASSISTANTS

Okay, you guys! I want that hole in the wall fixed in twenty minutes—or else! Get to it!

END

The secret of success in business lies in creating **a** market for a product. Today, a really clever manufacturer can use a little imagination, a little horse sense, a big advertising agency, and a lot of conniving to create a market for his product (regardless of whether one exists or not) by a sneaky trick known as

SUCCESSFUL MERCHANDISING

OR

HOW TO STAY IN BUSINESS

with one crumby product

HERE IS THE ONE AND ONLY PRODUCT MADE BY FINK, INC., OF OUTFOX, ME.

BUILDERS

There is No Substitute for

FINK CEMENT BLOCKS

STRONG . . . GUARANTEED . . . STURDY

erect economical foundations, walls, and enclosures for

HOMES   OFFICE BUILDINGS
SCHOOLS   GARAGES   FACTORIES
PRISONS

$40.00 Per 100   18"x12"x12"

FINK INC.

"THE FIRST NAME IN BUILDING SUPPLIES"   Outfox., Maine

AND HERE IS HOW FINK, INC., SUCCESS-FULLY MERCHANDISED THEIR PRODUCT BY CREATING NEW MARKETS FOR IT THROUGH IMAGINATION AND ADVERTISING.

Every Backyard Patio Should Have a

FINK

OUTDOOR
FOOTREST

Made of Weather-Resistant
Natural-Finish Cement
Delivered In Time For Your
Next Barbecue Fish Fry
Will Rest Any Size Foot

ONLY $7⁵⁰ EACH

Write Fink, Inc., Dept. "OFR", Outfox, Me.

FINK

"THE FIRST NAME IN OUTDOOR FOOTRESTS"

164

LARGE BOOKS
A PROBLEM?

THEN YOU NEED **FINK** HEAVY-WEIGHT BOOK ENDS

Guaranteed Not to Tarnish
Will Outlive Your Books

Send Money To:
Fink, Inc., Dept. "H-WBE"
Out fox, Me.

only 5^{00} **a pair**

FINK

"THE FIRST NAME IN
HEAVY-WEIGHT BOOK ENDS"

TRIM INCHES OFF YOUR WAISTLINE

with a

Fink

EXERCIZOR

- No Electric Shocks
- No Moving Parts
- Takes up Little Space
- Cheaper Than Bar-Bells

only $4⁹⁵
COMPLETE

Don't Delay! Send Check or Money Order Today To:

Fink, Inc.,

Dept. "EX", Outfox, Me.

FINK
"The First Name In Exercizors"

170

END

Lately, money-hungry Hollywood producers have been selling a new gimmick: cheap, bloody, violent gangster films with a 1920's background. Of course, blood and violence are not exactly new to Hollywood, but these guys have something else up their sleeves. Namely,

MAD GOES TO A
GANGSTER

Hello, there! My name is Ira Schlock. I'm a movie producer. The movie we are previewing today—which I produced yesterday—deals with a modern American hero—er, sorry—violent thug named "Fink-Face" Fester. Because "Fink-Face" was such a despicable character, I decided to treat him with proper Hollywood contempt. Mainly, I had a title song written about him, which Doris Day sings while the credits are being flashed on the screen!

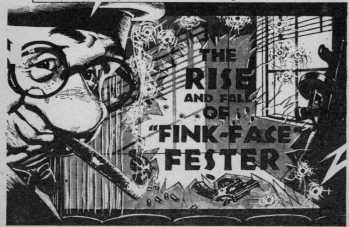

THE RISE AND FALL OF "FINK-FACE" FESTER

under the pretext of teaching a moral lesson, they are appealing to the vicarious thrill-seekers by making heroes out of Al Capone, John Dillinger, Baby-Face Nelson, and the entire Board of Directors of Murder, Incorporated. You'll see what we mean as

MOVIE PREVIEW

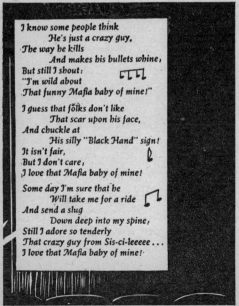

I know some people think
        He's just a crazy guy,
The way he kills
        And makes his bullets whine,
But still I shout:
"I'm wild about
That funny Mafia baby of mine!"

I guess that folks don't like
        That scar upon his face,
And chuckle at
        His silly "Black Hand" sign!
It isn't fair,
But I don't care,
I love that Mafia baby of mine!

Some day I'm sure that he
        Will take me for a ride
And send a slug
        Down deep into my spine,
Still I adore so tenderly
That crazy guy from Sis-ci-leeeee . . .
I love that Mafia baby of mine!

I've learned that the best way to give respectability to a cheap gangster movie is to have a well-known national figure introduce it. Since I've already used the President, the Vice-President, the F.B.I. chief, and Art Linkletter in my 635 other productions, this time I had to settle for Senator Lem Pivnik of Idaho!

My fellow citizens. This being an election year, please allow me to wipe the smirk off my face in order to say in all sincerity that we must wipe out Al Capone, John Dillinger, and other criminals who have been dead for years, to make this country safe for better things . . . like more gangster movies. The picture you are about to see is true—only the story is fictitious, to protect the producer from losing his money! At least I think so! I haven't seen it! And nothing on earth will make me!

When a gangster movie begins, it's always wise to show our hero—er, pardon—thug as a young boy. In this way, we expose the psychological reasons for his starting on a life of crime, which is always impressive. Also, we get in some early bloodshed, which is even **more** impressive!

Sorry, Mom! Sorry Pop! But I gotta plug yuh! Not because I want to—but because my home life is terrible, you both hate me ... and mainly the folks out there are rootin' for me to do it!

But Fink-Face son—we don't hate you! We love you! We'll do anything for you!

Shut up and die in agony, Bessie! You want to nip a promising career of murder in the bud, and give him some sort of healthy complex?

And now for Fink-Face's first big meeting with **Al Capone**. Whenever I **show** big lovable Al in my films, I make sure to hold up on the dialogue for ten or fifteen minutes to allow for the **cheers** and **applause** to die down . . .

Hi, Mr. Capone. I'm Fink-Face Fester. I'd like to join your swell Mafia Social and Athletic Club. I can do anything, take minutes, play punch-ball, kill judges. Whaddya say, Mr. Capone? You wanna initiate me? I don't mind going under the mill, Mr. Capone, Sir!

Shaddup-a you face, and-a let the sick movie fans inna audience finish applauding me, you fresh kid, you!

Awright! Ten-a minoots is up! Now we can-a talk! So you wanna join-a da Mafia, eh, fresh kid! Okay! I like-a you! You gotta nice cruel mout'! But mostly I like-a de way you don' look-a me inna eye when you talk-a to me! At's a good sign! Pick up a tommy gun anna some bombs! I gotta little job for you!

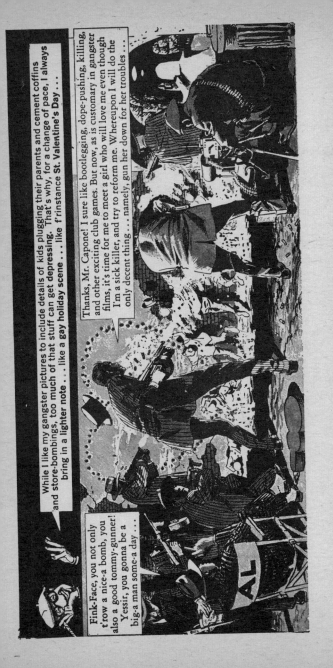

By the way, in case you're wondering why I'm the **only one** in Hollywood making gangster films of the 1920's, the answer is simple! I have a great social conscience, I have a fantastic talent, and mainly I **bought up all** the old box-type automobiles, old-fashioned upright telephones, and double-breasted suits **available** . . .
Hey, Fink-Face! I like-a your bomb-t'rowing style! You got-a class! You gonna go places some day!
Shucks, Mr Capone! That was lefty! Wait'll you see me throw righty! I got curves, sliders and everything! Gee, I like this work! You get plenty of fresh air, and you don't have to stand on corners and meet the wrong kind of people!
Hey, how come "Gutsy" Famisht didn't come along on this job?
His double-breasted suit's in the cleaners! How would it look if he threw a bomb in a single-breasted suit? The audience would laugh him off the screen!

179

Although it's nice to please the **romantic** movie-goer with a **love scene** in a gangster film, you've still got to hold the attention of the **violence-lovers**, and five straight minutes without violence can be **dangerous**. To be safe, this time I tried something different . . .

Baby, when we kiss like this, I feel so good I could do all kinds of wonderful things, like climbing mountains, and swimming oceans and shaking down candy store owners for protection money!

Oh, Fink-Face, you warm, wonderful, crazy Mafiosa! When you press your scarred lips to mine . . . I have marvelous thoughts. Like us getting married . . . and us having a family . . . and you taking your heel off my cat's tail and stop trying to sneak in some cheap violence!

After Fink-Face does the decent thing—taking his foot off the cat's tail and gunning down his girl—we switch to the big scene where all the Underworld greats have a meeting. Naturally, they come into the room one at a time, so that the audience can cheer wildly at each entrance . . .

'Scuse-a me, gentlemen! Before we get downna business, I like-a you all to meet Fink-Face Fester. He's-a good boy, an' he's-a gonna be an important thug some-a day! Fink-Face, meet-a da boys!

184

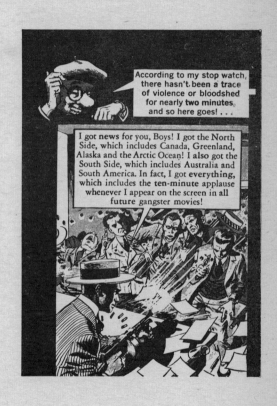

According to my stop watch, there hasn't been a trace of violence or bloodshed for nearly two minutes, and so here goes! . . .

I got news for you, Boys! I got the North Side, which includes Canada, Greenland, Alaska and the Arctic Ocean! I also got the South Side, which includes Australia and South America. In fact, I got everything, which includes the ten-minute applause whenever I appear on the screen in all future gangster movies!

But, as all of us public-spirited gangster film producers know, he who lives by the sword must die by the sword. And so, after two hours of showing him leading an exciting, profitable, and enviable life, I now demonstrate that "Crime does not Pay" by having Fester die a horrible and violent death at the very end!

See, Kelly! When you live the rotten, cruel, mean life of a killer, you have to die violently!

It's horrible! Cut down in the prime of life—at 103—by a bad case of measles!

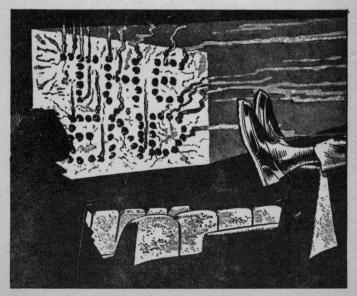

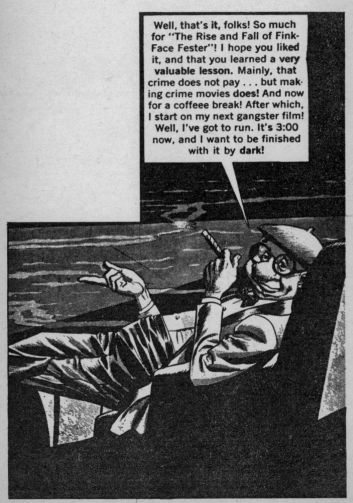

For his parting shot, Don Martin tells about the time he used quick thinking to save somebody's life while working with

THE
MOVING
MEN

END